My Dear Believers,

My name is Kate and I am Queen of the fairies in all of the world. I am also the head of The National Fairy Council here in Fairy Valley. The reason I am writing this letter to you is to firstly thank you so very much for giving a human home to a fairy! And secondly to explain a little more about who we are...

Many years ago I, along with some of my fairy friends discovered that there were fairies living with human families. Although their numbers were very few, as soon as word spread about how happy these fairies were, each one of us longed for a human home of our own. You see fairies thrive on the belief humans have in them and the magic that we can create in their homes. We believed then and still do now that every family should have a fairy in their lives. We searched far and wide for the right humans to help us and were so happy when we found the lovely people in The Irish Fairy Door Company! In return we promised to start sharing insight into our world, a world full of imagination and magic.

We have devised a Lease Agreement for both fairies and families to sign before they start to live together. It is a very informative document that we feel is super important for us all to live in harmony. Everyone in the family must sign the Lease Agreement and of course your fairy will need to too. We also like to send out reminders and alerts directly from Fairy Valley to all our fairy families. So please don't forget to register your fairy's name on www.theirishfairydoorcompany.com to ensure that you don't miss any important information that you may need.

Having a fairy living with you is the single most memorable and magical experience your family will ever have... All we really ask is that you love us and most importantly believe in us. Fairies thrive on a human's love and belief. Now only one question remains...

Do You Believe?

Yours in fairyness,
Queen Kate

Fairy
Welcome Guide

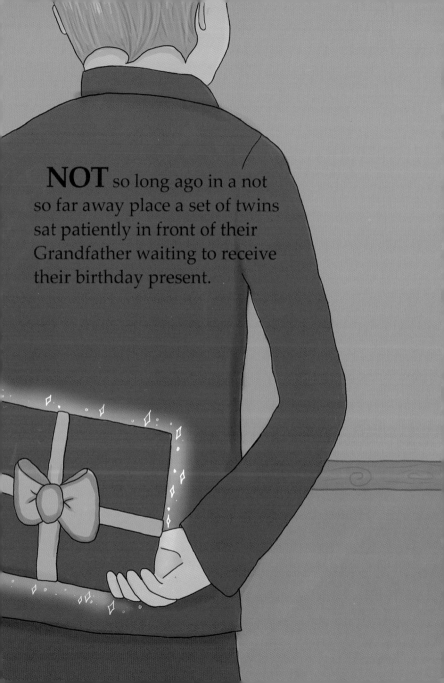

NOT so long ago in a not so far away place a set of twins sat patiently in front of their Grandfather waiting to receive their birthday present.

"Now Daisy and Danny, I think it's time.
This is a very special gift. It is something
that I know you will have forever"
said their Grandfather handing
them each a gift wrapped box.

The children's eyes lit up with anticipation as they each took their gifts and unwrapped them.

"Oh wow, this looks great!" Daisy said, peering down at the little door in the box.

"But what are they Granddad?" asked Danny excitedly.

Their grandfather sat forward a little in his chair.

"These are fairy doors," he smiled. "Once they are in place, a fairy of your very own will come to live with you forever."

The children were amazed and leaned closer to their grandfather so as not to miss a single word he was saying.

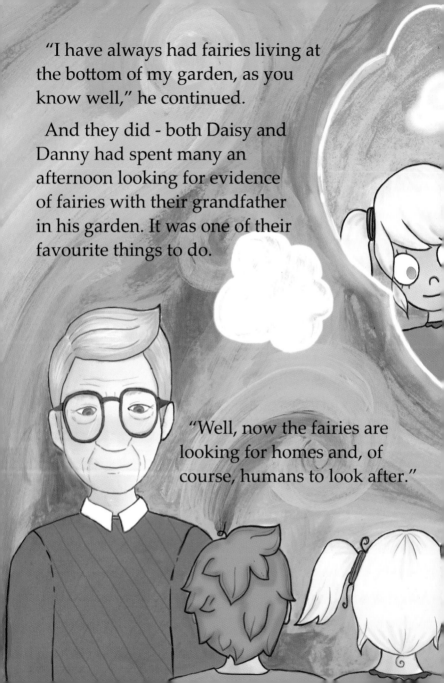

"I have always had fairies living at the bottom of my garden, as you know well," he continued.

And they did - both Daisy and Danny had spent many an afternoon looking for evidence of fairies with their grandfather in his garden. It was one of their favourite things to do.

"Well, now the fairies are looking for homes and, of course, humans to look after."

The twins gasped with delight.

"Do you mean that real fairies will actually come and live in our house, Granddad?" asked Danny.

"That's exactly what I mean, young man!" their grandfather replied, smiling from ear to ear.

"So, let's get to work," he said and stood up. The children remained right behind him.

First of all, with help from their grandfather to stick each one into place, they decided where they would put their fairy doors.

Danny stuck his fairy's door to the
skirting board while Daisy chose to
fix hers to the window sill.

Once in place, the three sat down to decide
what names they would give the fairies. Daisy
decided she would like a girl fairy and that her
name would be Primrose.

Danny thought it would be good to have
another boy around the house, so he wanted
a boy fairy named Jacob to move in!

Their grandfather explained that there were certain things that needed to be done before their fairies arrived…

"It is very important that we let Queen Kate and all in Fairy Valley know that your doors are in place and that we would like a boy fairy and a girl fairy to move in."

Fairy Valley

"How do we do that?" the children asked.

"For this part we'll need your mother or father," he explained. He called the children's mother and filled her in on what needed to be done.

Register Your Fairy

Choo

All four of them then sat down at the computer, logged onto www.theirishfairydoorcompany.com and registered the names they had chosen for their fairies in the Fairy Workplace Log using their secret codes.

"Now, this next bit is very important", said their grandfather.

"See these little bottles with the keys inside? Well, we need to leave them out for each fairy so that when they arrive they can use them to magically open their door and move into their brand new homes."

"But how will we know if they have arrived?" the children asked.

"Why, their keys will be gone!" he told them.

"From then on Primrose and Jacob will keep their keys with them at all times."

"We mustn't forget to leave the Lease Agreement out for them to sign when they arrive. Of course, every human living in the house needs to sign it too," he explained.

"You see, fairies are very well trained. They attend Fairy School to learn all about how to be a good House Fairy. Having a list of rules and regulations that both fairies and families need to agree on in order to live together happily is very important. Let's read them together!"

As he read the agreement out loud, Daisy and Danny listened carefully and nodded after each point. When their grandfather was finished reading they all signed their names quickly and left each Lease Agreement beside both of their new doors.

Their grandfather went on to explain that because their mother had registered their fairies' names, she would now receive an email every week with exclusive stories, messages and play ideas directly from Fairy Valley. These stories and activities would make it even easier to interact with their fairies.

The children had now joined a community of believers who together shared a love of fairies and all things magic!

That night, the children were so excited they found it hard to sleep. At first light the next morning they bounced from their beds to go see if their fairies had arrived and picked up their keys. They raced to find their grandfather.

"Granddad! Granddad!
They're here! Primrose
and Jacob are here! The keys are gone!"
squealed Daisy and Danny with joy.

Their grandfather rubbed his eyes and put his glasses on.

"Ah… and so your magical journey begins, children. How truly wonderful!"

From that day on Daisy and Danny would write to Primrose and Jacob often - asking them questions, telling them stories and drawing pictures for them – and, of course, the fairies would write back.

Each week news, stories and activities would come directly from Fairy Valley too.

Daisy and Danny's world was now bursting with imagination and magic forever more!

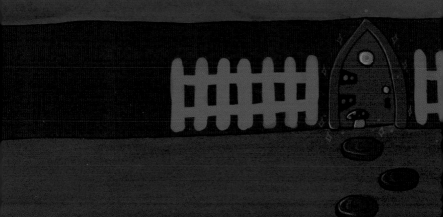

Would you like your very own fairy to move in to your home?

All you need to do is believe…

Your Fairy Certificate

My name is

_____

&

My fairy's name is

_____

He/She moved in with the

_____ family

on _____ 20 ___

About The Irish Fairy Door Company Founders

Aoife & Gavin Lawler

Our writer Aoife spent 16 years working for the Health Service Executive in Ireland but always dreamt of writing books. When Queen Kate and her Council came looking for help in telling their story, Aoife was the obvious choice. With a strong background in sales and a true entrepreneur,

Gavin has a talent of spotting a good opportunity when he sees it. Gavin was one of our first believers so when Queen Kate and her Council asked for his help in finding human homes for fairies he was happy to oblige.

Niamh & Oisin Barry

Our spokesperson Niamh worked as a Montessori Teacher and previously ran music classes for under 5's. She has lots of experience working with young children and truly loves it. Helping Queen Kate tell her story is a true honour for her.

Oisin has worked in finance for many years and is also a born entrepreneur.As the Fairy Finance Controller he is in charge of making sure that everything gets done as and when it should. Helping to find the right fairy for the right human is very important to him.

THE IRISH
COMPANY™

Visit us at www.theirishfairydoorcompany.com
/theirishfairydoorcompany